MY JOURNEY TO ANTARCTICA

CROSSING THE FIRST DOME

CLAUDIO NOCELLI

CLAUDIO ÁNGEL NOCELLI

Nocelli, Claudio Ángel

My journey to Antarctica : crossing the first dome / Claudio Ángel Nocelli. - 1a ed -
Ciudad Autónoma de Buenos Aires : Claudio Ángel Nocelli, 2024.
180 p. ; 16 x 23 cm.

ISBN 978-631-00-3380-8

1. Ovnis. 2. Ciencia Ficción. 3. Novelas de Misterio. I. Título.
CDD 910.4

WEBSITE:

https://nosconfunden.com.ar/

YOUTUBE:

*https://www.youtube.com/
@nosconfunden*

2ND YOUTUBE CHANNEL:

*https://www.youtube.com/
@nosconfundieron*

INSTAGRAM:

*https://www.instagram.com/
nosconfunden/*

PERSONAL INSTAGRAM:

*https://www.instagram.com/
eddienosconfunden/*

CONTENTS

INTRODUCTION

The following story could change the perspective of how we look at the world, just as I previously published the story of the great navigator W. Morris and our contact with his daughter Helen ("The Navigator Who Crossed the Ice Walls") who continued to send valuable and unique information. I believe that this voyage may be of relevance and that it is the perfect time to tell it in detail. Although, it has great incidence with the texts of the ancestral humans and all the movements that have been arising in recent years, I must also admit that this story found me at a very difficult time in my life, in every sense.

But, we will talk about that later, now I want to present you the story of a magnificent journey that seemed to be totally fortuitous but finally you will understand that it was not at all, and just as it used to happen in those epic voyages of the years 1750-1800 when everything seemed to emerge again and a new humanity was also emerging, this trip would have obtained so much notoriety and prestige among the great navigators, as those that crossed the Antarctic barriers that few dared to navigate and that until then, seemed impenetrable in the frozen waters of the south, generating a great challenge that some were willing to carry out, but this trip in the full modernity, with the technology that we have and that we still do not know, can, I believe, deliver another type of message in this frenetic and volatile world that we live in.

From the next chapter I will simply let you dive into this exciting story that will finally transport us to the doors that seem to exist in the Antarctic polar circle and that is jealously guarded and hosted, so at least, we are left with these pieces of a puzzle that we have been trying to put together little by little for some years, with the help of ancestors like Helen and her father William, with the stories that we can still tell today, and that they also helped to encourage me to tell this story, now I would be in charge of expressing in ink the memories of this indelible destiny to which we are heading.

CHAPTER 1- THE PLAN

I will summarize as much as I can in this part of how I ended up on a nameless ship on the most frozen shores you can imagine. One July 8th I got some boxes of mail, in one of them was a totally dark box that had no return address or P.O. Box, nor did it seem to be addressed to me or rather to anyone.

I hesitated first to open it, in fact, I waited several days, but the uncertainty and anxiety managed to convince me, then I opted on the morning of July 10 to open the box, besides I could not afford not to open correspondence when I already knew something about the ancestors and the way they sent information (although they always sent someone to deliver it by hand).

The box did not seem to have folds, it was perfectly closed and had a cube shape, on the back it had a small square in light blue that stood out against the black giving the sensation that it even shined, when I ran my fingers over the cube diminished light blue color I realized that it had some relief, then I opted to try to peel it off before opening the box, or maybe that was the way to open it? I was trying not to break anything inside, as the box was quite heavy.

When I removed the tape that covered this part, underneath there was a green logo, it seemed to be of some company or organization that I had never seen before and that I did not know at all.

Inside this logo appeared two words: "Corpus Etericum" (Etheric Body), if the box itself generated intrigue in me, now it was intermingled inside me with those mysterious tints of the unknown.

I then began to imagine that the postal service had gotten confused and that this box was not addressed to me, but again, since it was inside my mail and so many similar things had happened to me, I finally opted to open it.

From the same hole that had generated this logo a perfect fold was generated to be able to open from below the same box that thus generated a kind of window and opening in its entirety, finally I was there in front of the unknown, very resistant leaves like golden colored parchments with black letters were waiting to be read by me, again I felt lucky.

On a normal sheet section appeared my name, "This story is expressly addressed to Mr. Claudio Nocelli, as part of thanks and..."

At that moment I imagined that this was really another story that would give us so much information to publish, one more that would take us to those remote Antarctic places and that those passages to the mysterious and no longer so unknown lands that await on the other side would live again in each one of us. In the same paragraph it clarified "I would like to invite you to join this great journey that will take you to the Antarctic continent..." Then a shiver went up my back, making my skin bristle all over, it would undoubtedly be the beginning of a unique journey.

CHAPTER 2 - THE JOURNEY TO ANTARCTICA BEGINS

The Empty Corporate Life

It was the month of November and I was very stressed by several jobs that I had to present, they were important dates for the company of which I was part and there were the well-known limits that marked the agenda totally transforming my life around. When that date was approaching there was no time to even sit down to breathe, anxiety and stress were predominant and played a key role even to not distract me while I sat down to reread contracts, piles of sheets, taxes and a lot of spreadsheets that had to match.

Between how overwhelmed I was, the sleepless nights and how physically unwell it all made me feel, the months went by very quickly and deadlines for deliverables arrived. My face showed that it had been at least 15-20 exhausted days and that I needed to finish as soon as possible to be able to rest in a decent way, the people around me noticed it, but those who knew me already knew that the time was like that for my current life.

The deliveries were finally made and everyone seemed to be very satisfied, in fact, I was called by important people within the company and others on several occasions to congratulate me, the happiness of my surroundings seemed to be endless, I had even put the company in an unbeatable position, everyone seemed to be enjoying the moment except me, I even spent nights reflecting on everything, although I was grateful for the fruits of my effort and work, on the other hand I found it all empty and without any sense, I even commented it with someone close to the same company in passing, but these issues are not generally taken in a good way by the most important heads of large industries.

The days went by, I was ready to rest and I expected to take a vacation soon, one morning before going to my office, I received a call from the person to whom I had told about the odyssey of my last days, and he told me that a person from a company called "Corpus Etericum" wanted to see me in person and that it was something quite urgent, The truth is that I was totally unaware of this company, I had never heard of it and since I worked with all the other organizations, it did not seem relevant for my partner to be so enthusiastic, I told him that I would still go to the interview so that he would be calm and then I forgot about it completely, until that day arrived.

CHAPTER 3 - THE ENCOUNTER WITH THE STRANGE ORGANIZATION "CORPUS ETERICUM"

THE JOURNEY BEGINS TO BECOME A REALITY

At 10 AM on a Tuesday before the end of November I receive a call from a person who said his name was Clark from the organization "Corpus Etericum", he invites me to a restaurant to meet him because he had something very important to offer me, I told him that I was about to leave on vacation and I even named my friend so he could go in my place instead, but he insisted that it would be a few minutes and that I had to be the right person to meet him because the offer had to do directly with me. I really noticed all this quite suspicious but it was not so unusual considering that the last deliveries had had such repercussion, I imagined that this person "Clark" was going to offer me some kind of job that I was clearly going to decline in a respectful way, but I did not think it was bad to go to such interviews since one can also be in good relationship with another company and in this way also improve the link when it comes to work, my position had to do directly with relationships and links with other people who lead companies.

In short, I agreed to meet at noon that same Tuesday, and I set out to perform tasks quickly, my mind was already thinking about the well-deserved vacation coming next week, and I could not wait to make the meetings that I had pending to close everything neatly and dedicate a little to me.

I arrived at the meeting and the place was completely empty, I sat at the end of a bar, I had never been to this place nor did I know the area, to tell the truth, I didn't really go out much, usually the meetings were held in offices.
So I waited there for this Clark guy while I ordered something to drink and took care of my cell phone, all the notifications I had generated more stress for me since it was work I had to postpone knowing that during my vacation I would be thinking about all the work I was going to have to do when I came back.
Clark showed up 5 minutes later than agreed, and suggested that we sit more comfortably at one of the tables by the window.

He was enthusiastic and told me that he was very happy to meet me, I asked him several times about this company or organization that I did not know, but without giving me much detail he told me that they were dedicated to the analysis of environmental data and did not want to explain much more, and that I insisted.

After a banal chat without much more, he told me that he wanted to offer me a trip and that he expected a "yes" as an answer, since it was a unique trip where I could not only rest from my daily routine, but also reach a point that few people had managed to reach, he really did not convince me at all at first and I told him that I had traveled a lot during my life, and many of those trips were for business, adding also that I was quite tired lately and that I was at a time where I preferred to stay closer to my home than anything else.

He said he understood me since he led a life similar to mine, but insisted on the trip, adding that other important people from different companies were also going to appear.

I really had no intention of traveling nor did I see how it was going to be fruitful for me or for the company where I worked, then he continued to tell me about this trip and told me that the destination was Antarctica, then everything before was going to give a complete turn, because it was a place I had always wanted to visit and I knew that its entrance was quite selective, from that moment my ears began to change and hear more about his proposal.

Clark added that the trip corresponded to show the importance of the environment and the right place was virgin lands like Antarctica, its environment, the studies that are carried out there, he told me that they were going to pay me good money and that the image of the company was going to climb with respect to the importance that we could show the world about the care of the environment and many other things that really did not interest me much, the plan to be able to make such a trip was not hand in hand with any company, but it was something personal, I wanted to get to that place for a long time, but what convinced me the most was the following phrase of Clark:

"You will go on a private ship, paid by our organization, it is not a cruise trip, nor a trip with a military ship that will leave you in some Antarctic base, this is something special, private and quite secret since you will reach points that very few have visited".

Without further ado, here was the point that motivated me the most, those opportunities were not given every day, I commented to Clark that I would think about it but that I was quite enthusiastic about the idea, anyway, I was not going to accept such a trip from an unknown company and I set out to search and ask about them in many places both inside and outside the company, we shook hands and agreed to keep in touch to see the possibility of arranging such a trip.

At that moment I did not analyze so much the consequences or dangers involved in such a trip, although I was still uncertain about the profit of such a company in which important members of different companies would make a private trip to those southern latitudes, something did not fit me at all.

I talked to my partner about Clark's offer, and he told me that it was quite common lately to take the committee of a company or companies on trips, especially if it was a company related to the environment and the protection of natural resources, in fact, he saw it with good eyes to increase the prestige of our company and the focus on the future.

I did not see it with business eyes, but on the contrary, as a different trip to an area that always attracted my attention and that few had visited, undoubtedly it was something that happened only once and I felt somehow lucky.

Time went by, the people around me had given me good references about the company to which Clark belonged, I had also seen good references on the internet and the desire I had to make this trip led me to accept Clark's offer, whom I notified via email and then by phone.

Clark told me that the trip would take place in early December and the boat would leave from the port of Ushuaia, in southern Argentina, so he would schedule a flight to Buenos Aires and from there directly to Ushuaia, but not to worry because they were going to take care of all the paperwork that needed to be done previously, as well as accommodation. When I asked if anyone else would be traveling with me from other companies on the same flight, he seemed to give me confusing answers or avoid the issue, so I didn't take it into account then either.

CHAPTER 4 - THE ROAD TO THE END OF THE WORLD

FROM BUENOS AIRES TO USHUAIA

The day of my trip had arrived, I had said goodbye to my companions and headed to the airport to catch my flight to Buenos Aires and there, after a few hours of waiting I would make the transition to the flight that would take me to Ushuaia, or "The End of the World" as it is known. I arrived in Buenos Aires with some turbulence but minor, and after a fairly comfortable ride I called Clark to finalize details and let him know I was waiting for the next destination.

Clark did not answer any of my calls, I thought it was something related to the signal, I also called the number he had left me from the company "Corpus Etericum" but it was "out of range", I figured then that everything was due to a communication problem between countries, and I did not give it much importance, anyway I had the next flight number and Clark would surely contact me before arriving in Ushuaia, anyway I sent messages to his number to let him know that I had arrived at my destination.

I boarded my next plane and at least looked several times at my cell phone for some response from Clark that they had not arrived, but instead, I had a message from an unknown number that said "VESSEL 212-HOH".

My feet finally touched the south of Argentina, and I took a cab to my hotel, the place where the company had arranged my one-day stay, and then boarded the ship to Antarctica.

Clark finally contacted me once I was settled in the room, to my peace of mind, he told me that it was probably due to a signal problem and that he was not aware that I had tried to communicate with him, but that he had received my messages, I also told him about this strange message about the ship number, and he told me that it had been sent by his company, that this would be the ship that would sail the cold Antarctic waters.

The first destination would be "Omega Island", a small island in the peninsula, from there the destination would be another one going around the continent passing by Port Lockroy, Vernadsky Base, Reunaud, Adelaide and after an extensive tour we would descend in the famous "Ross Island" and we would settle in Mcmurdo Base to, from there, get ready for our last destination, another trip to the interior that he could not detail me for the moment.

The mystery about a trip I was about to make, where few had arrived, in an unknown and difficult to track vessel through frozen waters did not really please me, especially since I needed to give the destination to my family so that they would be reassured, but Clark reiterated that he apologized but that it really depended on the weather and that once there on the boat, we would know everything about the final itinerary. After a not so long talk with Clark and then with my family, I got ready to rest because besides being quite exhausted by the flights, I also needed to recover energy for the next day's big trip.

CHAPTER 5 - EMBARKING ON A MILITARY VESSEL TO OMEGA ISLAND

THE 212-HOH VESSEL

I left the hotel very early in the morning, the sun was just beginning to rise, a black car was waiting for me at the door, and it would take me to the port, which was really very close.

A huge cruiser was there, as well as several boats, I looked for some identification with the "212-HOH" that had been assigned to me, but I found absolutely nothing.

A person with a blue cap approached me asking for my name, and then asked me to accompany him to a large dock, he came back to me and said, "there is your ship sir", it was a gray military vessel, which had no insignia or name.

Some other people were also waiting to board, or so I assumed, so I approached and asked them.
They spoke fluent English, but I could tell they were not native speakers, they told me they were from different companies across the continents. I was relieved that other people like me were about

to start this journey with me.

I spoke for several minutes with a person who identified himself as Carl, who was also very excited about the journey we were about to take.

There were military personnel inside the ship, as well as some people who said they were scientists and that they were going to accompany us to our first destination, "Omega Island" and that there they would divide the group, since there was another group waiting on that remote island.

Once we all entered, the boat quickly left that port, without any delay, I said goodbye in the distance to the beautiful lands of

Ushuaia that I had not been able to spend so much time but I promised to visit them again soon to enjoy a long stay.

Once we were away, a drizzle began to fall along with the fog that existed by then, the view of the city was no longer on the horizon, I felt some fear of this whole trip, but I had to enjoy this unique experience, plus the people on board were very warm and everyone was in jubilation.

CHAPTER 6 -
STORM AND SWELL,
DEPARTING FOR
THE ANTARCTIC
PENINSULA

The timid drizzle was starting to turn into a big storm just 45 minutes after we had left the port, our cell phones had no signal, and the boat was starting to move a lot, I tried to think of other things as well as talk about business and banal topics with my fellow passengers.

The military men inside had asked us some questions before leaving, but they were helpful, but not the four people (two men and two women) who said they were traveling to join the ranks of the Antarctic bases and the geological and meteorological study they are carrying out there.

In December in the southern part of the continent is when the day is the longest, since it dawns around 4.30 AM and stays until 22.30, I had noticed it the day before, but, although it was 13.46 the sky was totally dark, I imagined it was because of the storm, but it is not that the day had darkened, but we were sailing only with the light coming from our boat, absolutely nothing could be seen beyond 2 or 3 meters outside.

One of the military men told us that it was common during storms like that, that there was nothing to worry about, but then he joked with his companions, and I could understand something like "They don't know everything that happens in these parts, better not tell him" and laughs that were shared by them.

Some of my companions gave in to the swell and preferred to sleep, not a bad idea since we still had a long way to go, but how was I going to sleep in the middle of the ocean under a storm and with the boat going from one side to the other? It really wasn't in my plans to close my eyes.

15.35 - The storm was easing a bit, although the swell was more intense, the military never seemed to have the option of turning back in their minds, I imagined they were going to keep that in mind because of the bad weather, but we were still on a steady course for the Antarctic Peninsula.

What I imagined would never happen to me, ended up happening to me in the midst of this strange swell and my nausea, I closed my eyes and ended up falling fast asleep. When I woke up I had no idea what time it would be, I looked at my cell phone but it was "dead", before sleeping I had made sure it had enough battery charge to last many hours at rest, I proceeded to connect it to the portable charger, but nothing, my phone showed no signs of wanting to answer, I wanted to ask other people, but everyone was sleeping, I then went out for a walk around the boat, in the darkness of the night, although it was difficult to elucidate on the night and day there.

CHAPTER 7 - CELL PHONES GO OFF

I ran into a military man whose name was Andres, I told him that my cell phone had died suddenly and he pretended to be surprised, but he told me not to worry because surely it would answer again once we got away from the storm that still generated in the distance, amazing lightning and with it a deep daylight invaded us. I was really worried about the idea of not having a way to communicate with the outside going to a place so far away, I then asked him how much time was left, and he told me that there were still many hours to sail, although almost no drops were falling, it was still totally dark outside.

Some of the people inside started to wake up, and they told me exactly the same thing, their cell phones were not working, they did not even turn on exactly like mine, the same person called Andres told the rest of the group the same thing he told me, that everything would work when we get closer to the Peninsula, and that there were several hours to go. We were given hot food and drinks, so then the weather in the interior returned a little to normal.

A few hours passed between chats and a little rest, plus some drinks to avoid the intense cold, we even went out to breathe a little, at one point I forgot my gloves and felt like if my fingers were going to fall off one by one because of the intense cold.

Reenan, one of the companions told us that his cell phone had finally turned on, then we all tried to do the same without luck, but along the way each one was turning on in his own time, we do not know why our devices did not work on the way to the "Drake Passage", I do not understand how I did not wake up during much of this particular journey, since according to what we were told later, we sail through waves of about 4 meters, although we were told that it can be twice as bad.

00.45 a.m. - One of the soldiers entered our sector indicating that there were 50 minutes left to reach our destination, we applauded with happiness, we were just an hour away from stepping on Antarctic lands, the excitement was once again igniting inside me, pure adrenaline, at that moment a great happiness invaded me for having accepted this trip and all the fears that I had felt during the journey began to slowly fade away to be forgotten.

The group was looking forward, with an overwhelming happiness, the destination was there, just 20 minutes away, we all went outside the ship, but the military personnel asked us to wait inside because soon we would arrive at our destination and the corresponding maneuvers would begin to reach the port, we could not really see much more than some lights that began to appear on the horizon, yellow and white lights were intermingled.

2:10 a.m. - Finally the military informed us that we had arrived at our destination, we all shouted with excitement, and applauding we prepared to descend, we had everything ready.

CHAPTER 8 - DESTINATION: LAMBDA, THE PROBLEMS BEGIN

Before getting off the boat we were asked not to take pictures, it seemed quite absurd not to be able to keep a memory like that, one of our group, Reenan, argued to the staff about this, after such a long trip and something unique like reaching Antarctica, were we not going to be able to take pictures of this trip?

The military told him that later he would be able to take the pictures he wanted but that in this area it was totally forbidden, I took the opportunity to ask where we were descending, thinking that I would say the small island Omega, but I was wrong, they told us that due to the weather they had to make a change of destination and that we were in "Lambda" which was close to Omega, but on the opposite side of the continent (According to the GPS on our cell phones, we were not in the area they wanted us to believe, but at the time we thought it was due to an error).

When we descended in total darkness, just the light of the boat and a faint light coming from the islands, we ran into the harsh climate, a devastating wind in conjunction with extreme cold almost made us run straight to the base, they made us enter some huge doors (they were easily 3 meters high), and then go down some very long stairs that led underground, then a not so long corridor and several doors on the sides, one of them opened and a person welcomed us.

It was Patricia, a very warm person who received us in a very friendly and helpful way, offered us food and showed us the rooms we were going to occupy for that night, or rather, for just a few hours.

Patricia told us that she had been working there permanently for 6 months, we asked her about the darkness during the day and about the fact that our cell phones did not turn on during most of the trip, but she played it down and made us focus on what we were living, that it was a unique experience that we had to take advantage of every minute.

I had left several messages for Clark, but my signal wasn't the best, my family hadn't received anything I had tried to send either. Patricia got a little nervous when she was asked about the issue of the photographs, commenting that the orders came from above and it was a matter of safeguarding the area and that it was not due to anything else, very strange that we were not allowed to take pictures outside.

We slept in closed rooms, without any light or anything facing outside, although the atmosphere remained warm and that was extremely important.

Just 4 hours later we were woken up because it was time to continue our tour, my cell phone read 7:02 AM.

We boarded our gray boat, now with some clarity, although under a heavy rain again. Patricia greeted us cordially, before we left she was with another group of five people who also gave us a cordial goodbye.

Reenan again had a heated discussion with one of the soldiers on board, he even took his cell phone to see if he had taken pictures, suddenly the atmosphere was rarefied on the way to the other destination, besides they did not tell us where we would go, the scientists had already descended and only my group was on board.

After a few hours, things calmed down a little, Andres who seemed to be the friendliest, again gave us food and drink to continue towards the uncertain destination of Antarctica, I asked again if he knew where we were going, but he left indicating with his face that he could not say, but then he told me that in a few hours we would arrive.

CHAPTER 9 - THE GRAY DOMES OF THE UNKNOWN ANTARCTIC BASE

The rain had stopped completely, finally, and lights of some bases could be seen in the distance, according to my companions this place was called "Lemaire". Again, I closed my eyes as I was very tired from the few hours of sleep.

When I woke up I am not sure how many hours had passed, but the others were still sleeping, I felt like a lot had passed since we left supposedly Lambda, the military personnel came in and told us to get ready to descend, we were arriving to the area they said we should and there they would give us instructions.

Instructions? I asked inwardly, I looked with my confused face to my companions, who understood less than me and had woken up with the shout of the military.
Our cell phones were not working again, only Reenan's, I don't know what he had done to get his device to start, and he commented that the GPS was not marking any destination or that it was erratic, it even marked impossible places, one of the soldiers saw that his cell phone was on and took it from his hands, Reenan wanted to get it back and another of the soldiers pushed him back, We were all surprised by this reaction, then a big discussion

started between our group and the military, they tried to calm us down, but Reenan was out of his mind, in fact the military that had taken his device threw it overboard before everyone's eyes, it was so big this brawl that one of them took a gun and shot in the air, then we were all silent, then commenting:

- "Listen gentlemen, here there are orders that must be obeyed, I am sorry that this is not a trip of children graduates, here certain rules must be respected, please now descend and follow the staff who will provide you with the necessary information to follow the plan".

We looked at each other and commented very quietly. What plan is he referring to? What the hell is going on here? Where did we come from?

The fear invaded my body again, from such a great excitement for the trip to a huge disappointment and now the despair of being so far from home, with no way to contact anyone and at the mercy of some military who were behaving in a lunatic way for leaving us incommunicado.

We descended before a totally strange landscape, nothing of what we expected to see in Antarctica was in front of our eyes. There were some kind of dark colored dome-shaped structures with lights underneath that illuminated the ground, there was still a trace of snow on the shores.
There was not much visibility in the weather, but behind them we could see some strange "antennas" crossing from one side to the other.

After the heated discussion with the military and Reenan losing his cell phone, the spirit of the trip had clearly changed negatively, we were all very serious, confused and worried, we descended from the boat and they put us in another kind of Base or Station, inside one of those big dark domes.

We went down again by some long stairs and although it seems incredible, we continued descending, but now with elevators to the -3 floor, as it was indicated there.

One of the ship's servicemen dropped us off in a brightly lit section of the "-3" floor and a man of about 55 years of age, with a big mustache and dressed in a white smock welcomed us.

He made a joke about our faces, and we told him what had happened, the man was sorry, but encouraged us to know that there were other times to come since "the adventure was just beginning", those were the exact words he used.

He introduced himself as Doctor Highs, and commented that all kinds of studies of the soil and others were carried out there in those islands, we asked him several times where we were, but he commented that for the moment he could not tell us since it was a secret place.

Again our bad mood increased, and now began a discussion with this gentleman about why they were hiding our whereabouts, several people in the group told him that they could not not inform us, were we kidnapped? Reenan asked, very exhausted by the whole experience.

Highs commented that none of that was happening there, that simply as we were traveling from one side to the other, there were sectors that could not be informed and that they received us as "Transit" but that tomorrow we would understand it since they were going to inform us about the whole final itinerary.

The six of us in the group left quite disappointed and confused to the rooms that they had arranged, unbelievably a few hours before we were happy to know we were going to have such an experience in Antarctica and now we were with the uncertainty of how we were going to get back home.

CHAPTER 10 - THE SECRET MISSION AND THE BLUE-SKINNED BEINGS

I fell asleep after reflecting deeply about this whole experience, I was looking for the sense, I started to doubt about Clark, about his company, about why they didn't answer my calls before taking my flights, I even started to doubt about my partner in my company, what would this company "Corpus Etericum" be? Maybe I should have done a deeper research and not be guided so much by other people, and a lot of negative thoughts invaded my mind, and it was not for less, since I was in an uncertain destination, without communication and far away from home.

I dozed for a while, without really being able to sleep deeply, there was a knock on the door of my room, the one I shared with Reenan, we were both indignant, and one increased the indignation of the other.
From the other side entered a person that we had not seen before, he had a very strange aspect, military clothing but not the common one, but one that I had never seen, his insignia was not known either.

He spoke to us in very harsh English, commenting that we should leave the room and follow him.

We took our things and left for outside, there were only the two of us, the other four of the group did not appear there.

We asked this person several times about the rest of our group and he commented the following:
- "Your companions have another mission".

Mission? We said in unison along with Reenan, What mission? The strange man spoke again:
- "Now you also have a mission, but please enter this dome to be informed".

We looked at each other with Reenan not really wanting to enter anywhere, but what else could we do? My partner had no patience whatsoever and had already proven it, but he entered first with no little desire.

Upon entering and descending the stairs, we found ourselves in a kind of military hangar, where there were easily 15 or 20 people, some military, others in white smocks (I imagine scientists), others were operating large computers, and in the background some men with dark balaclavas but their skin seemed to be of a bluish color.

If there was a stranger panorama that my mind could imagine, it was nothing like what we were living, we looked at each other with Reenan without understanding absolutely nothing, we simply did not believe what our eyes were seeing.

The man who guided us here then told us to sit and wait and that they would be here soon. We stayed in a small room inside that same hangar waiting while our confused minds tried to process what we had seen, we didn't even want to externalize it with words.

Long minutes had passed and no one came for us, we didn't really care so much about the wait, it was more the uncertainty of not knowing what was going on in there, and who were those blue-skinned beings that we had seen wearing a kind of black mask that at first I imagined it was some kind of balaclava but then we analyzed it with Reenan and it looked more like a kind of mask, neither of us dared to leave there to observe a little more, much less after the problems we had been having with the military up there.

From one moment to the next a person who called himself "Saul" appeared, and asked us to stay calm, without even asking him anything, he informed us that it was common to panic, feel fear, or any other similar sensation, but that we would get used to it as the days went by, that's when I decided to interrupt him;

- Sir, we don't understand anything of what is happening, we were brought here in a simple tourist trip and through a company...

The military man now with another tone interrupted me saying:

- Well, it seems to me very well, surely you speak to me of "Corpus Etericum" Am I right?
We both nodded our heads.
- "I need you to understand the seriousness and commitment of this matter," Saul said again, adding, "This is where it's going to happen".
then he said, "Things are going to happen here that you may never have seen before, and beings will come that have never passed through your eyes before either".
What kind of beings? We asked almost in unison along with Reenan.

- "Beings you will meet later, but now pay attention, please".

Our faces showed dread by then, and clearly Saul could tell, I imagine it was a situation to feel that way, what had we really gotten ourselves into? We should be walking around and taking pictures on the Antarctic Peninsula, and now we're stuck in a hangar underground and surrounded by "bluish beings" ...

CHAPTER 11 - WE
ARE IN A WAR ZONE

"I'm going to level with you right off the bat, comrades," Saul said, "You are in a war zone right now".

What? What do you mean, war? What kind of war? We began to ask.

"A war, period, you will know that in due time, but, to sum it up, it is a war between good guys and bad guys, and we have studied your backgrounds to know you well enough to know which side you are going to play on".

And who are the bad guys? I asked, for a moment I wished this was all part of a joke played on the tourists here, but what kind of tourists were coming to these shores? I couldn't even confirm what part of Antarctica we were in. Besides, the beings there were real and their height seemed to be well above average.
"The bad guys are the ones trying to kill us, for now it's more than enough to take them as enemies, what do you think sir?"

- I would have loved to give another kind of answer, but I guess I just nodded my head, both Reenan and I were dumbfounded, suddenly in a few hours we had been thrust into a military hangar full of strange beings, military and scientific, and plunged into a strange war between two factions we didn't know and being honest we also didn't care at that moment at all.

"Now rest" Saul said, and asked us to follow him to new stairs and another new basement to leave us in a gray and light blue room, quite large with two beds.

The moment Saul closed the door, we tried to come to some conclusion with Reenan, but it was really hard to describe the whole scene we were living, besides, how were we going to keep an eye with all this going on around us? We didn't even know who we were in the hands of and on which side of the supposed conflict we were, we felt kidnapped in an inhospitable place and far away from our lands.

The way they had abruptly brought us here, the little information and all the experience we had had made us really doubt the good intentions of these characters, as well as we began to seriously question if we were on the "good" side as Saul had put it, but we had a long night and an arduous next day that would surely mark us forever in our lives.

CHAPTER 12 - INFILTRATING "UNKNOWN LANDS" ACROSS ANTARCTICA

Early in the morning Saul interrupted with knocks on the door;

- "Upstairs comrades, it's time to go" he shouted from somewhere else.

Reenan was with his eyes open and in blood, he had not slept at all, I had fallen asleep an hour ago, we were both in a painful situation and exhausted, but, the adrenaline of not knowing what was coming I think helped us to stay alert.

We followed Saul who took us back to the room inside the same Dome of the previous day, a blue-skinned being passed in front of us, he was about 2.50 meters tall, he exceeded us by far, even Reenan who was 1.90 meters tall.

I didn't hesitate to ask Saul along the way about who these beings were.

Saul again answered vaguely about that, but commented that they were beings that were helping us in this conflict, and that, if it were not for them, none of this would exist.

I wanted to ask again, but we had already arrived at "Dome C" as they called it and two more people were waiting for us.

They introduced themselves as Victoria and Romuel, they said they were there to study the area and told us that they had to make a trip to continue with the study, and that for some reason, they needed our company, that we would go to lands that were "beyond the ice" and the area where we were, and that we were going to have to get there and present ourselves as simple sailors who had arrived at their shores by chance, the idea of the plan was to obtain all possible information about the place and the civilization that was there to deliver it to them through communication devices.

- Excuse me, are you saying that there is "a civilization" living in lands beyond Antarctica? Reenan asked.
- "Not in Antarctica, but beyond the Antarctic Walls, we have the exact location, and we know that there is a large civilization in the lands behind the ice barrier".
If anything was missing to make this whole experience even stranger, it was to learn about the existence of a civilization in remote lands that do not appear on current maps.

Reenan then pressed the issue:

"And why should we infiltrate there, why don't you go?"
Victoria smiled and replied about it being a secret matter and that they had already tried to do it, for some reason that she did not want to elaborate on, she commented that we were the chosen ones to make this trip and that all the information we get was crucial for humanity, since we were all in danger from this "great civilization that attempted against peace", those were her textual words.

Then I entered the conversation saying:

"Excuse me but, we were brought here for a field trip and it turns out that now we are chosen to infiltrate distant and inhospitable lands that on top of that You don't want to enter?"

Victoria answered now in a bad way claiming that such statement was not true, and that they had been making efforts and studies for a long time already, and that they needed us to do our part to help all humanity, she also added that "this work is not for us, not even for you, it is for all humanity inside, for your loved ones, for everyone".

Reenan and I started to doubt about the whole thing, and if it wasn't for those blue beings that didn't look human at all, we would have thought that it was all a bad joke or that everyone on this base had gone crazy.

Opposing the idea of the trip did not seem a good option, they were really hostile to us (I think that even the trust had been broken since day 1) for that reason we agreed to make the trip that would be done in a few hours, Saul asked us to get ready again and to go get our backpacks (which had been left in the underground room).

All this bordered on the unbelievable and ridiculous at the same time, we wondered with Reenan why they chose us, simple businessmen, in a supposedly so complex security task that included all humanity, something did not fit at all and we were suspicious.

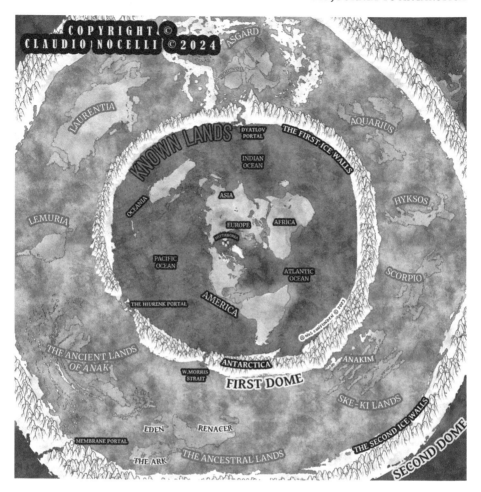

CHAPTER 13 - THE MICROCHIPS IN OUR BODIES

It was two hours after they came to pick us up, now one of the blue beings was in the group, this strange being with scaly and bluish skin, with its big and yellow eyes, gave a very bad vibe and the sensations were horrible when being close, but for some reason we kept very calm.

He gave us some dark devices that had a red button in the center, Saul told us that we should keep them in the right nostril of our nose, the truth that again I was starting to miss my home so much and the regret of this trip was greater at that point, even now I had to introduce some kind of device through my nose, things were getting worse.

Once we went through all this process, which was surprisingly painless, Saul told us that now they could see through our eyes and hear as if they were there, all this would have surprised us even more if we were not already living so many incredible and abnormal situations that we took it quite calmly.

They then showed us on a kind of projector that this blue being had on his right arm, that our eyes were now acting as two cameras recording everything, and according to them, we were now ready to make this trip to those unknown lands that crossed the Ice Walls.

They told us that first we would travel by helicopter to an inland area that was still ice, and then from there on that same coast a small boat would take us to our destination.

Now everything that we thought and wanted to externalize with Reenan, were going to remain only in glances and for our interior, since they listened and saw absolutely everything, the situation was becoming more and more uncomfortable every second.

The helicopter that picked us up was totally dark, and when we were rising I could see better the whole area where we were. And that hangar that gathered a large amount of snow around it had colossal dimensions, without even contemplating that it had at least 10 floors underground and the large amount of people working there, it would have to be extremely important.

The pilot did not even welcome us nor did he participate in any talk, and so we left for the first destination together with Saul, that coast where we would get on the boat.
Saul was calm and quite benevolent, he offered us several things since we accepted the trip, he seemed to be more concerned about our well being all of a sudden.

Reenan was bursting into a deep grumpiness, I think he was going through this whole experience even worse than me, who wanted absolutely nothing to do with any of this.

We were two lab rabbits where they were experimenting on us, and that the whole experience from now on was going to be recorded by our own eyes, plus we didn't know where they were sending us, they were talking about a big war and we were supposedly going to "enemy land".

CHAPTER 14 - CROSSING THE ANTARCTIC PLATEAU AND EMBARKING TO THE LAND BEHIND

Arriving on the other side of the great plateau, the weather seemed to be a little less harsh, the cold was not so intense and even some vegetation could be seen.

There was a small port and several boats, most of them military. There were also dome structures there in gray, and other smaller hangars, none like the previous one.

Saul gave us more information about what we should say, and what was forbidden to talk about, he stressed the importance of the trip and that our families were also in danger, he used all the psychology possible to torture our minds with deep fear so that we would not move away from the plan.

He told us that we should simply act as two sailors who happened to end up on those shores, that we should observe and ask as many questions as we could, and that it was even possible that they could help us in the return to the dividing ice barrier.

We asked him several times what would happen if they did not believe us, but he omitted any answer, we began to understand more about the seriousness of this whole matter, we were involved in something too dangerous and we did not know how we were going to end up, since we were totally unaware of this "civilization" that lived behind the Antarctic barrier.

We finally embarked, this small boat was quite modern, it had radio equipment for direct communication with one of the operational bases and also a radar system, but Saul informed us that we should not touch absolutely nothing since everything was armed according to the plan, in less than ten minutes we left the coast towards the uncertain destination, those coasts of a lost civilization of which we knew absolutely nothing and with whom we were supposedly at war.

With Reenan we didn't need to talk, just looking at each other was enough, we were two strangers living the same experience that had already become torture since we stepped on the Antarctic Peninsula, two people who were in the middle of a big conflict and we had no idea how many people this involved, besides, if we really thought all this, we were being sent to our death since Saul knew very well that we had only a one way ticket;

Why would they believe our story when we had microchips that were recording from our eyes? If it was an advanced civilization as we were informed, they would know about our plan right away, and our luck would run out there, no one would rescue us since the ones sending us there had no intention of us coming back.

CHAPTER 15 - CROSSING THE "INVISIBLE BARRIER"

THE SECOND SUN APPEARS

Our destination suddenly turned to the right and then took a sharp turn to the left side, the giant barrier of ice and plateau that we were leaving behind was barely in our sight while the sun shone in the distance, another small object appeared on the horizon on the opposite side, reddish in color, was it our imagination or were we in the presence of two suns?

Suddenly without being able to explain it in words to describe the sensation, our body seemed to be pushed by a great force from the back of the boat, everything seemed to move suddenly before us for a few seconds, as if we had reached some maximum speed, I would not know how it would feel to be in one of those supersonic aircraft, but I think the feeling was similar, at least I thought so.

Once all this strange experience was over, we looked back and saw how a strange invisible wall came back to "recover" after we went through it, it was as if we had caused a kind of transitory gap that was completely covered seconds later.

Reenan talked to me, and once our boat got far enough away from the Antarctic barrier and this new invisible barrier, somehow, sensing that there would be no return we started to talk about the whole thing even though we knew they would be watching it all.

We were in a rage against those who had put us in this situation, so we started to come up with various plans in case things got really tough out there.

In case they knew we were recording from our eyes because of their technology, we could confess everything, what could we lose? We didn't really know what we were facing, but we already knew the beings that had sent us here as an experiment, we were really in the most absolute ignorance about what would be best for our lives and in what way we could save ourselves, I guess it all depended on what we would find there.

Reenan tried to change the course of the boat in a very risky move, we did not know the waters we were navigating at the time, but he claimed he knew something about navigation thanks to his father. As we tried to change our course an alarm went off inside, we looked at each other in terror and knew then that they still had control over us.

The trip continued on its fixed course and approximately three hours later we sighted land. Reenan raised his arms in a kind of warning to those inhabitants, who from afar watched us in confusion.

No port or large structures could be seen, only some white domes shining under that strange red Sun.

CHAPTER 16 - THE ENCOUNTER WITH THE GIANTS OF THE UNKNOWN ISLAND

Some people began to gather when they saw our small boat arrive, these people were gigantic in size in comparison, they were between 3 and 3.5 meters tall, and thus, we were even more fearful of reaching these shores.

Anyway, there was little we could do as our boat was still preparing to take us there by force, once it touched the shores of this "new civilization" there were already easily 25-30 people gathered around the white sand.

Reenan and I met in a glance and without a word we were both equally stunned, What now? I asked inwardly. Most of these beings had long curly reddish hair, their complexion was very white and their eyes were deep blue, although there were other features, what I have just described predominated.

The first person who came to welcome us was a giant that was almost a body length apart, she looked down as if we were two little toy dolls, she stretched out her hand to, I assumed at that moment, give us a welcoming handshake.

Then I took her huge hand for that greeting, she said a few words looking back in an indecipherable language, and the others laughed for some reason we clearly did not know.

Then two people arrived with different clothing, something like part of a militia, and with more serious faces, they spoke something with the woman and then one of them in a strange English asked us to follow him.

As we walked behind these two men, we were asked questions: Where are we coming from? Why were we sailing close to the Ice Barrier? Was the expedition conducted on our own? And a host of other questions.

As we walked I was clearly very nervous about the situation of this interrogation, I had a feeling that they were not going to believe us and really the plan of telling them everything at first was not the best option either, besides, although the people had received us quite well, these two men did not seem to have much patience.

We walked through a very well kept path, a lush forest glimpsed around us, I could see several birds that went from one place to another, a very quiet place with few people, at least in that area, it seemed that we had been directed to a village.

The Giant then asked us to enter one of the structures they had there, it was one of the largest "white domes" that interfered with the beautiful path we were crossing, so we entered with Reenan and then we went up some stairs until we found a kind of office.

CHAPTER 17 - THE GIANT ANAKIM LEADER CALLED HONI-RU-KI

We waited seated for some minutes, the chairs were very comfortable, and this structure seemed to have a greater dimension inside than what it appeared on the outside.

Another person entered the place, with different clothes (very elegant), he had a face similar to what one knows as "Orc" or what we know from fiction, his face was rigid and emanated an angry and hostile appearance, but the experience was totally different and even ended up inspiring confidence.

He was very happy for our visit and told us that they had had some visits from "new humans" in their lands but never in this sector or region, he also told us that everyone was aware of the situation and that they were going to help us to have a better stay, he asked us again where we came from and what we were doing sailing the frozen waters of the south of our continent.

With Reenan we looked at each other several times and I think we were about to go ahead with our plan to tell him everything about our microchip implants and that we were recording absolutely everything, but we did not dare and besides, it was still too early to do something like that, we could generate an irretrievable break in our trust and maybe then we would end up in some kind of dungeon.

This man introduced himself as Honi-Ru-Ki and also spoke English in a very basic way, but he made himself understood, he also told us that they spoke a local language that they developed over time to what it is today. He also told us that they had the blood of giants but that they had suffered serious genetic modifications over time and that they also had part of a "previous humanity" inside them.

 This part at the time we did not fully understand, they were moments of absolute confusion for our minds, with the passage of time then we were investigating and learning a little more about their culture and their past.
As well explained by Honi-Ru-Ki, who was the leader of that region called "Honrota", he explained to us that his ancestors came from the Anakim Giants, but, "not purely" but from those who had escaped precisely from our same lands, and that many cultures there knew them as "Patagones".

These giant beings intermingled with humans, and also suffered serious genetic modifications due, as he explained to us, to the "modified environment" inside the First Dome.

- First Dome? Reenan interrupted.

Exactly, you had to cross this Dome to reach our shores, otherwise your ship would have possibly disintegrated with you inside, there are some passages to cross it and not all of them have the same fate, this Dome covers and envelops all the continents you know or most of them at least...

- Does it have to do with this "Invisible Wall"?

Yes, so that you can understand, it acts as a membrane that may or may not let the matter that decides to pass, that is why there are sectors of entry and exit, if you had navigated, for example, 1 kilometer further north or south you would not be here talking to me.

We looked at each other with Reenan surprised by this, obviously ours was not part of luck but rather of a previous programmed navigation by the military.

He even added a very curious phrase that at the time was very complex to interpret: "Do you like the stars in the heavens? You're going to miss them here, because you won't see a single one.

Honi-Ru-Ki continued explaining a bit about this strange Dome and about the climate and environment that is manipulated inside, but he did not want to detail us about who or who was carrying it out.

He then went back to talking about his ancestors and told us about ours as well, saying:

"You will be able to know more about your past, so many lies were told and we know it, we know your lands well believe me, but there are many other things that I cannot mention, at least not for the moment, you are just coming out of there and it is not good for your mind to "attack" you with so much information all at once, but your ancestors, the humanity before yours also live near here, in fact we have several ancestral humans living with us that you may know, I understand that you have many questions and who better than one of them can answer about what they have had to go through to continue living, there is a very big conflict that you don't know about".

At this point Reenan took the initiative and asked

- Conflict, is there some sort of war going on then?

"Unfortunately yes, it is an invisible war for most of you, and just so it was ruled so that you are not aware of what is going on in there for so many years, but as I said before, time to time, then you can know more about this and other issues, I welcome you and count on me for whatever you need, I hope your stay is the most pleasant and please try our fruits that only here are obtained and I do not know any mortal that has rejected its taste".

We shook his hand and cordially withdrew from there, it had been the best welcome we had ever been given, and we really didn't expect it, had they believed our whole story? Together with Reenan we felt very bad to be recording all this, we felt that we were helping the enemy, for with all the cordiality and kindness that the leader here had presented himself, we could not feel that we were against him.

One of the giants that guided us there was present again and asked us to follow him out, telling us that we would now meet with "one of our own", we imagined then that we would be facing one of the most incredible meetings we were going to have in our lives, if true, we were about to talk to the same previous humanity, which we still did not know why they called it that way. While all this was happening together with Reenan we were looking at a map that was on one of the walls with all the areas that made up these beautiful lands.

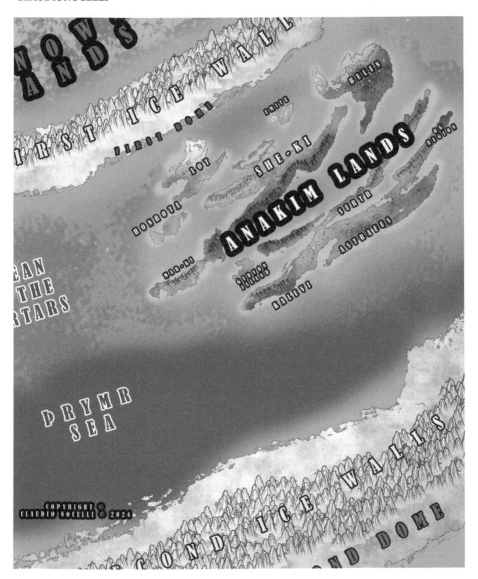

CHAPTER 18 - HELEN THE ANCESTRAL WOMAN AND THE APPRENTICESHIP

A woman with a youthful face approached us, she was wearing a kind of monocle, but of a totally opaque shade with blue lights on the right side, and she was the first person who measured less than the rest there.

She greeted us cordially in perfect English and told us to call her Helen, she also added that she had not seen humans visiting there for a very long time, at least not from the "new humanity" she detailed, although she commented in passing that her father came from the same lands but she did not want to go into it at that time.

We were able to ask her about this "new humanity", what did they really mean?

And she explained to us without so much detail that there had been several humanities throughout time or "single timeline", and following that, then she could say that we belonged to the last one, while for example she belonged to the previous one, and they were the ones who escaped from the "Known Lands" before the "great flood" and after the "Great War" that was unleashed there.

With Reenan we were on a kind of roller coaster of information, it was all very difficult to digest, although we tried, the whole experience was magnificent and terrifying at the same time.

- Big war? Among whom?

"Among the same as now, it never ceased, with the difference that now there is no great civilization there inside in the lands where you come from, since "the Cuijas" annihilated them almost completely as well as their great nuclei-centers".

-Who are the "Cuijas"? We asked almost at the same time.
"Cuijas, Custodians, Sun-Gods, whatever you want to call them, are those who detest the whole humanity and manipulate them completely, as well as all their environment, in fact, they make them sick and for that reason their lives are shortened, as well as the lives of so many other beings".
She also added "We, for example, in the time of the ancestral humans we lived much longer, as well as here in these lands, your body will be purified over time of all the toxins that you can bring at this time inside you, they also took care of genetically modifying your bodies in each reset".

CHAPTER 19 - RESETS
IN OUR WORLD

- Reset? I asked

"Sorry, I did not explain it in detail, anyway it is too early for you to understand it, the resets in broad strokes are those carried out by the Custodians to end the development of a human civilization, it is almost always carried out with great floods, the last one was known as "the mud flood", their pyramids help to carry it out, these pyramids are creations of other parasitic accomplices called "Anunnaki" and together they carry out this almost total annihilation. They leave only a few babies that they have in their big laboratories to start all over again, that is why we differentiate humanities between several cycles.

- Was it always like this? Since when are we under this parasitic domination? Reenan asked.

"It was not always like that, no, the first humanity had among its main objectives the absolute liberation of all beings, this first humanity began in the famous lands of Asgard and from there they were developing all their power towards nearby lands, unfortunately they were surprised by these parasites and there began our absolute decline, but I do not want to extend this story much more, your confused minds will thank me, take these fruits and go to rest, take advantage of the peace that lives in this area, you have come to lands where goodness abounds and we fight the dirty parasites that you have just left behind".

 These words were very strange for us, somehow, we began to suspect if they were aware of our implants and that we were recording everything, for a moment it seemed like an experiment. We ate the most delicious fruits that anyone could have ever tasted and we were guided to some very comfortable rooms where the reflection of that strange sun entered through its large windows, the coast could also be appreciated, some giant beings walked through their large fields and their children ran happily from one side to the other, absolute peace was breathed in these strange and distant lands.

CHAPTER 20 - ABOUT THE WAR BEHIND THE ANTARCTIC BARRIER

My bed was next to Reenan's, neither of us could sleep a wink, everything we were living seemed to be taken out of a science fiction movie, from a simple tourist trip to Antarctica to end up talking to Giants and Ancestral Humans about the lost history of our ancestors, all this was an extreme madness that we could not yet digest completely, besides we felt that we were betraying them, when we saw their children running happily through those fields full of peace we thought about this "Invisible War" and what those military men with the "Blue Beings" could do if they came here for some reason.

Although we also thought that these giant beings might be hiding a lot of information from us, and it wouldn't be bad either, since we were the newcomers who were also sending information to the force.

Hours later we were surprised by rumbles that could be heard outside together with terrible tremors, I fell from my bed with an immense dread, I looked at Reenan who had his eyes open looking towards nothingness itself, I shouted his name several times and tried to move him, Reenan had died, without knowing the reason nor understanding what was happening but with immense pain and fear I left that room totally dejected.

More bombs seemed to fall around, in fact, one of them had hit so close that had bent much of the structure from which you could see the outside, many beings were running from one side to the other, I could not analyze anything of the situation, just try to get out of that place and hopefully meet Helen, the only familiar face.

I was lucky to be alive since the structure where I was had been totally destroyed minutes after I could get out of there, Reenan had died during his rest, but what had killed him? I did not understand what had happened and my new brother was gone forever and I was left on this remote island with unknown beings and in the middle of a war scene.

A whole army of Giants had moved into the area and was driving away the attackers through the air as well, I began to doubt about this "sudden attack" and I began to qualify it as being engineered by the same people who had sent us here, I felt guilt as I believed that this attack had come after I had recorded much of this sector. I started to run towards the opposite side of the biggest conflict, and also where big families were heading, I noticed some humans there and I did not hesitate to approach them, among this group was Helen, and I was so happy to see a familiar face that I almost ended up hugging her.

Tears were falling from my face and she tried to calm me down, I told her that Reenan had died during our break and she explained that it could happen, and that all this was due to crossing the dome, it is one of the factors, she tried to explain to me as we walked along with the group in a hurry that, when crossing this invisible barrier, the pressure and the sudden change of environment can cause in some people serious problems, and without realizing it Reenan had suffered this.

We had to leave the place quickly and thanks to the great planning, administration and seriousness that those beings seemed to follow in those lands, everything was done quickly, but efficiently, we were put on large boats to get away from the island, while many blue ships crossed the skies and some were braided with accurate shots, the dark ships fell like birds into the ocean, wrapped in flames.

CHAPTER 21 -
THE RELIEF

THE IMPLANTS IN MY BODY

I felt so much guilt and was so overwhelmed by the situation that I set out to tell Helen about the whole microchip implant, I needed to relieve this backpack that weighed tons on my shoulders.

I waited for a chance for just the two of us to be calm, then that same night under the darkest sky I had ever seen, I told her the whole truth.

Helen just smiled without saying anything else.

Then I explained again in case she hadn't understood, "I feel responsible for everything that happened, I feel it's partly my fault for not telling her from the beginning".
Helen stared at me and told me to be quiet, that everyone there knew about it and that they had deactivated it as soon as they had arrived on those shores.

- How so? I asked in surprise
Then she explained to me that they had a radar system that was in charge of monitoring all kinds of implants for each visitor and that nothing after having descended from the small boat could have been recorded or decoded, in fact she even doubted if it had recorded anything after we have crossed the passage of the first

dome, since such technology does not always work as they expect, there are several towers that they have on the island, as well as in the large cores there to deactivate any kind of attack.

Clearly it does not always work since they had received a sudden attack that had not been read in time, but that had nothing to do with me or Reenan and our microchips.

I really felt one of those reliefs that compares to absolutely nothing, and now I really did feel totally part of them, I had no doubt that I was on the right side, again my tears started to fall as Helen touched my shoulder and said "Now that you know, you can rest easy, your time here has just begun".

Then I took the opportunity to ask about the place where we had been sent before arriving to these lands, but she assumed that they were simple bases of some kind of organization of some part of "the dome" that had direct connection with these beings "Custodians" and that from there they initiated all kinds of research on lands behind the "Antarctic Barrier", and they were very interested and desperate to learn more about the technology that seemed to be superior, at least for now.

Later I would also learn that these sudden attacks were not common but every now and then they happened and that for that reason in those lands they lived in constant alert, the set of lands and islands that made up the whole area were called "Anakim Lands" or "Lands of She-Ki", as Helen explained to me, She-Ki was considered a leader of the whole region and that she was on a journey that I could not comment right now.

Also these "Anakim Lands" were composed of the "Lands of She-Ki", Honrota was the area we were about to leave behind, Mar-Ki, Lot, Emite, Belen, OG, Surtr, Geryon Islands, and then the islands that were close to the "Sea of Þrymr", and the Lands of Astraeus, in each area lived Giant beings that differed greatly from each other genetically and therefore, I was going to find many differences in their physiognomy, and also many ancestral humans lived in the different regions.

CHAPTER 22 - NEW DESTINATION: THE LANDS OF LOT

After a very long journey in those immense ships we crossed the deep sea to reach a region far to the north, which they called "Lot's Lands" and to get there we had crossed "the Path of the Dark Depth" since they said that its waters were as deep as any other nearby region.

To the north there were some remote islands far from their

continent called "Scorpio", although there was no prohibition to sail its coasts, from what I heard it was not advisable to walk in those latitudes.

The structures of "Lot" were magnificent, I could not describe the architectural beauty of those buildings and the lights dazzled me with a unique beauty, there was an abysmal difference with the town we had left behind, although it was not considered a big city, it was noticeable that there was a large population here.

The citizens of this region welcomed us and were aware of all the suffering and attack we had received, therefore they were even more helpful, they gave us all the comforts in their homes, as well as the leader Honi-Ru-Ki did not rest until the last being had the necessary comforts and was welcomed by a family or empty place he could find, obviously that same night we ate with them in a meeting as the great families they were.

That night, in spite of the deep sadness and melancholy of the whole situation that was lived, moments of great peace were lived and all the goodness that reigned there gave me the sensation that another kind of world could exist, without so many conflicts, I also began to believe that the Custodians really rot everything they touched.

Helen stayed with me long hours of the night even when the families of giants went to their rooms, we took a walk along the shores of a rocky beach, another of the humans who was in the group of the boat also joined us, his name was Anthony, he was a young man born of ancestral humans who had also escaped from the known continents.

I was able to learn that night that several plans were being carried out to liberate humanity from there that was not aware of anything, as I was just a few days ago, of all this manipulation and invisible war between these beings "Custodians" and the Ancestral Humans in conjunction with the Anakim giants, more than 2000 spiritual masters had been sent to raise awareness to the great humanity and although the plan had worked at the beginning, then everything was vilely manipulated by the reigning parasites to contaminate the messages of deep empathy and love, then everything was vilely manipulated by the reigning parasites to contaminate the messages of deep empathy and love, the operation was then called "Portal Dome-Breaker", and there were also other missions of which it is better not to expose at this time but of which I was terribly surprised.

CHAPTER 23 - ABOUT DEATH AND THE 178 WORLDS

They also helped with the sadness that my heart had for the loss of Reenan, they explained to me the path that "The Source" or human "Soul" makes when disembodied and returning to the "Celestial Lands" and some of what happens there also. I also felt peace for all those who were not in this plane, as well as what our future holds, this experience in this plane was magnificent and had to live it every second, the conversation with these two ancestral beings changed my world forever and another energy seemed to resurrect inside me, we usually live off between the daily routine and daily obligations, worries about money, health, care for others, all this takes us away from breathing and enjoying the beautiful details that life itself provides us.

Several white dots illuminated the sky at times, a very dark sky, and they told me that they were ancestral ships and that they belonged to the Anakim, some were also technology from another world called "Cassiopeia".

- How many worlds are out there? Then I asked

- 178, Helen replied

- 178 Worlds! I exclaimed then, very surprised

There are 178 known worlds inside this "Great Dome" but there are other worlds that were discovered very recently and we don't have much information yet.
Then she showed me on her forearm a device that she turned on and by means of a blue screen she made me see some maps and details of these other worlds that surround us.

After this, and being very overwhelmed by everything I was learning, we went to rest in one of the homes that a family had given us, I would rest in one of the small domes they had inside, although it would not be for more than two hours, no one sleeps more than 2 or 3 hours in those lands.

I woke up exhausted, but I could not complain, the previous night had completely nourished my mind and my understanding of the world around us and the history of mankind, and also compared to the terrible morning of the previous day, it was a day to try to continue understanding the whole experience that I had to live.
How would I get back home? I asked myself over and over again in my mind, almost like those bells of an old church that echoed within me sharply.

I did not see the way to return without the help of the Anakim or the Ancestral Humans there, but would they be willing to risk in this way for an unknown like me? It was impossible to return by my own means, I had neither the capacity nor the necessary transportation, besides in case I could cross the Dome by the same providence, what could I find on the other side but enemies or military hunting people like me returning? Those blue beings that later I understood that they were the same "Custodians" were not going to let me return and have the life I had before normally, my life had taken a sharp turn and changed completely, I doubted then that I was going to return, at least not in the near future.

But what about my family? They would make a deep search,

they would talk to my company, who would also surely affirm my trip to the frozen waters of the south, I think that all that would involve several people who clearly would not take it well, something of their plan could be exposed and that would also endanger everyone.

All that in fractions of seconds my mind had imagined, and then, on the advice of the ancestors, I tried to calm down and quiet the inner voices a bit, which many times pose scenarios that do not come to fruition. Then I would tell Helen or Anthony about my return home.

CHAPTER 24 - THE MEETING OF THE ANAKIM LEADERS

Time went by, and the ancestors there had calmed my anxiety about my family and the things I had left behind, they were in charge of sending messages to my family to let them know of my whereabouts (the exact destination would not be given as that would put them in danger) but it was enough to let them know that I was well, for the moment I could not return to my lands but they were about to start a new mission and obviously I signed up to be part of it, so then it would be a way to be able to visit my brothers.

Although Anthony did not agree with me being part of the plan, as he considered it risky and feared for my life, it was not good for the bodies of the new humanity to make such a transition several times in such a short period of time, especially since my body was beginning to purify itself of all the toxins it brought from the known lands. For that reason my application was not accepted, for the time being, they promised to consider me very soon.

Helen spoke with the leaders of the many regions that were meeting to discuss the future and carry out plans and movements in this "invisible war", and got me permission to be part of this new operation, which, by the way, did not seem to be easy.

I met a few days later or "Suns" as they called here, and I

contributed my bit about what these structures were like, the types of hangars and beings I had seen there, and not much else, I was worried about the implants they had done because, if I went back there, how would they impact? They told me that once they had deactivated them, it was impossible to recover them, and that they could try to extract them, but it would be risky, so for the moment I preferred to leave them in place.

The other fear was clearly the fact of crossing the First Dome twice more, considering what had happened to Reenan, and they reassured me saying that once I had crossed the first time and had had no reaction, it was hardly going to happen even if I crossed several times in the same day, therefore, everything was ready to undertake such a mission.

Again it was time for my learning, every day there was learning something new about our environment, this new operation included the rescue of humans from the known lands to the lands of the Anakim, but, they had to be people who were carrying out the changes and processes necessary to cross the dome, otherwise they ran risks as we did with Reenan that something like that would happen.
The processes of cleansing or purification of the body began with the people who were going to be part of the rescue, as long as they agreed, there were few people who had not reached the level of manipulation to accept such a change of life, simply the Custodians in conjunction with the dome of humanity had a whole system to bring down all spiritual ideas and the potential that each human had for "The Source" or "Soul" that existed within them. For that reason, this was carried out with great care by the thousands of ancestors who still operated there in order to initiate, through one of the operations, a rescue to new lands on the other side of the Barrier or Dividing Membrane.

As I learned later, besides a physical cleansing, another great form of cleansing could be carried out through spirituality, empathy and help for the rest around, this generated a chain change in the environment creating problems in the previously programmed custodial system, thus expanding small changes that moved away from the "automatic processes" that had also been created in the bodies of the new human leaving the "custodial simulation" that we call "Earth".

For that reason, there were at least a hundred humans living in the distant lands called "Ancestral Lands" to the east of where I was, I had never yet had the pleasure of meeting, but it was in the plans when I returned from the operation that was to take place the next day.

CHAPTER 25 - OPERATION RESCUE OF THE NEW HUMANITY

How was I going to help in this Operation? I was simply going to provide peace of mind to the humans who were going to initiate said Dome crossing, as a personal experience having managed to do it without even being aware of it, I could be the main link that would provide confidence to those who were going to carry it out, besides there were not many "new humans" who wanted to return to the lands of origin once they settled on the other side, the risk was extremely great.

My life had changed completely in a very short time, although speaking of "time", it is very strange how time passes here, and according to what I was told it is totally different from the time that passes inside the first dome, there inside everything happens "faster" to try to explain it somehow, the years pass faster and it increases, therefore, if I meet my family I could find that time passed much faster for them than for me, if we take the same timeline.

March 8, 2024, 19.53 hours marked in my diary. My last hours here inside the first dome, in the beautiful lands where I was born, we are carrying out the mission as agreed, without inconveniences, I was able to visit my family since the Ancestors made all the movements so I can see them and melt in a deep embrace with each one of them, since it is possibly the last time I will return. They cried when they saw me, but I welcomed them with an indescribable inner peace and an immeasurable smile.

I explained to them a little of the knowledge I had acquired and of the transition when we leave this plane, I tried to calm them down and gave them all the assurance and confidence that I was well, I added them to the list to prepare them in case they ever want to cross the first dome safely, but I did not see them so convinced of this.

I also believe that these will be my last texts here from this side, I fervently believe in the ancestral desire and the goodness of the Anakim that the future can be better and that we can turn these lands into the beautiful peace that the lands on the other side transmit, that our children can be born and be happy surrounded by harmony and that empathy can be the nexus to a better world, but of course, all this can be carried out without the dirty parasitic hands of the Custodians and all those who prefer to be on their side even against the will of their own brothers, these will be my last lines from here, on the other side there is good, that looks at you and protects you from so many injustices, nothing will be in vain, start the process of kindness, empathy and believe in your infinite spiritual potential, we are in contact.

TERRA-INFINITA MAP

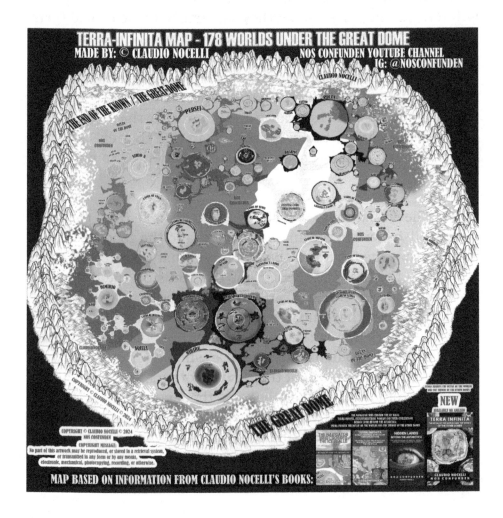

ABOUT THE AUTHOR

Claudio Nocelli

Born in Buenos Aires, Argentina,
Lover of occult stories since I was a child, I followed the skies closely after spending hours reading about UFOs and everything related to extraterrestrials. But something did not fit me in those interstellar travels until the story of the navigator would finally dispel so many doubts, in addition to the ideas of ancient books of mythology and travel that created a possible connection with lands and planets behind the Poles, everything began to have another perspective and sense, especially regarding the human past and the infinite spiritual potential.

Creator of the YouTube Channel: "Nos Confunden" and "Nos Confundieron" with more than 8,000,000 views

Author of the following books:

-"The Navigator Who Crossed the Ice Walls: Worlds Beyond the Antarctica"

- "TERRA-INFINITA, Extraterrestrial Worlds and Their Civilizactions: The Story told by the Woman who was Born in the Lands behind the Ice Walls"

- TERRA-INFINITA Map

- Lands of Mars: 178 Worlds Under the Great Dome

- Lands of Custodians: 178 Worlds Under the Great Dome

- Hidden Lands Beyond the Antarctica: The Continuation of Morris' Journey between Interconnected Planets

- TERRA-INFINITA, THE TRILOGY

- TERRA INFINITA, The Detail of the Worlds and The Theory of the Other Domes

- The Navigator Who Reached the Sky-Projecting Walls

BOOKS BY THIS AUTHOR

The Navigator Who Crossed The Ice Walls: Worlds Beyond The Antarctica

The story of navigator William Morris who, after the Independence War in the United States, decides to investigate with his new vessel the waters surrounding the Antarctic Circle, finding an unknown passage to an open sea. Other lands await him behind, along with another civilization, the story will begin to reveal to the entire group another reality based on the true past and future of the human being. It will finally lead him to the discovery of other worlds behind the Antarctica and most importantly to know himself, a unique journey from which nothing will ever be the same again.

Terra-Infinita, Extraterrestrial Worlds And Their Civilizations: The Story Told By The Woman Who Was Born In The Lands Behind The Ice Walls

The story told by the woman who comes from the lands behind the ice walls, in the "Ancestral Republic", daughter of the navigator William Morris, who will provide information that was hidden from us for a long time about the worlds that are crossing the poles and the secrets of extraterrestrial civilizations. We will also be able to discover the human history before the Last Reset and the continuation of what happened to her father when he returned to our lands. This can change everything.

Hidden Lands Beyond The Antarctica: The Continuation Of Morris' Journey Between Interconnected Planets

Helen Morris, the daughter of the navigator born in the lands behind Antarctica, gives us more details about the continuation of her father William's journey, the Giant-Humans and the hidden petrified trees, the importance of returning to our lands, the contact with other beings coming from other Planet-Domes and the stories and secret information kept in the Great Ancestral Library. Each chapter gives us more clarity about the worlds and civilizations that surround us, this story will immerse us in a unique journey into the human past and future and above all an inner journey into our true human essence.

Terra Infinita, The Detail Of The Worlds And The Theory Of The Other Domes

Welcome to the knowledge of the TERRA-INFINITA in all its dimension, the Great Dome or the Great Barrier-Membrane will break forever to give way to the "Other Domes" that await behind, another new barrier overcome in such a short time.
The Ancestral Humans with Helen as their new leader set out on an unprecedented adventure to blaze unexplored trails in their travels that will open doors that have never been reached before. With the help of Hiurenk's technology they will transport us to other worlds and new horizons, we will learn the details of each one of them from the Great Ancestral Library Database, as well as the new contacts with beings from other Domes that surround us.

The Lands Of Mars: 178 Worlds Under The Great Dome

178 Worlds Under the Great Dome - Volume 1 - The Collection of

the hidden Books about lands beyond the ICE WALLS

The lands of Mars hide much more than we imagine, here we can read the stories of the origin of the Martians in conjunction with the ancestral expeditions of the humans who live behind the Ice Walls.

Lands Of Custodians: 178 Worlds Under The Great Dome

In this book we will begin to learn more about our colonizing enemy.

Who are the Custodians? How did they come to colonize so many lands? Why have they gained so much power?

This parasitic race does not seem to want to leave our lands nor let us know our true history and essence.

We will also take a journey into the past to learn about part of our origin and the importance of the "human soul."

The human being from the research and its subsequent results seems to have become the preferred race not to let it escape and set as its main mission to manipulate it to the point that it can not develop to its full potential, as this could be of great danger to the custodial race in their desire to continue to have the same power over these and all the lands surrounding this Great Dome.

The Navigator Who Reached The Sky-Projecting Walls

Is it possible to imagine encountering other worlds by crossing the Ice Walls?

But before reaching this conclusion, if possible, how could they be accessed?

The following story immerses us in a unique journey that can give us details of how it could be at least a part of these strange walls and their connection with the First Dome and the sky we see every day, different from what we may come to know as "the Great Ice

Walls" near the famous and mysterious Antarctica, and above all can answer those questions about how a mind could be corrupted simply to seek their own power or feel powerful in front of the rest regardless of the consequences.

Made in the USA
Monee, IL
30 July 2024